Georgia O'Keeffe

2005 ENGAGEMENT CALENDAR

Pomegranate

Catalog No. Q201
Published by Pomegranate Communications, Inc.
Box 808022, Petaluma, California 94975

Available in Canada from Canadian Manda Group
One Atlantic Avenue #105, Toronto, Ontario M6K 3E7
Available in the U.K. and mainland Europe from Pomegranate Europe Ltd.
Unit 1, Heathcote Business Centre, Hurlbutt Road, Warwick, Warwickshire CV34 6TD, U.K.
Available in Australia from Hardie Grant Books
12 Claremont Street, South Yarra, Victoria 3141
Available in New Zealand from Southern Publishers Group
P.O. Box 8360, Symonds Street, Auckland
Available in Asia (including the Middle East), Africa, and Latin America from
Pomegranate International Sales, 113 Babcombe Drive, Thornhill, Ontario L3T 1M9, Canada

Pomegranate also publishes the 2005 calendars *Georgia O'Keeffe* (wall and mini wall), *Edward Hopper; Wolf Kahn; A Small, Untroubled World: The Art of Gustave Baumann; Ben Schonzeit: Flowers; Rothko, and Alfredo Arreguín.* Our products and publications include books, posters, postcards and books of postcards, notecards and boxed notecard sets, magnets, mousepads, Knowledge Cards™, birthday books, journals, address books, screen savers, stationery ensembles, and bookmarks. For more information or to place an order, please contact Pomegranate Communications, Inc.: 800-227-1428; www.pomegranate.com.

Cover image: *Red Canna*, 1923
Oil on canvas, 30.5 x 25.1 cm (12 x 97/8 in.)
Pennsylvania Academy of the Fine Arts, Philadelphia
The Vivian O. and Meyer P. Potamkin Collection, 2003.1.8
Estate of Vivian O. Potamkin

Designed by Mariah Lander

Dates in color indicate federal holidays.
All astronomical data supplied in this calendar are expressed in Greenwich Mean Time (GMT).
Moon phases and American, Canadian, and U.K. holidays are noted.

● NEW MOON ☽ FIRST QUARTER ○ FULL MOON ☽ LAST QUARTER

One of the first female painters to achieve both widespread popularity and critical acclaim, Georgia O'Keeffe (1887–1986) completed more than 2,000 works of forceful and compelling beauty, leaving a legacy that forever will resonate throughout the world of American art.

O'Keeffe first garnered commercial success during the 1920s and 1930s, through her sensual flower paintings and the series of portraits that photographer and art collector Alfred Stieglitz took of her. After traveling to Taos, New Mexico, in 1929, the Wisconsin-born artist was so enthusiastic about the light, the colors, and the expanse of the desert landscape that she eventually moved to New Mexico. There, over the following sixty years, she devoted her creative energies to capturing the forms and essence of the land, capturing images of bleached bones and desert scrub.

Throughout her long career, O'Keeffe constantly experimented with abstraction and color. The twenty images of flowers and land-scapes reproduced in this calendar reveal the range of O'Keeffe's talent through the late 1930s. They are fitting tribute to the creativity and vision of one of the country's most extraordinary and revered artists.

2005

JANUARY

s	m	t	w	t	f	s
						1
2	3	4	5	6	7	8
9	10	11	12	13	14	15
16	17	18	19	20	21	22
23/30	24/31	25	26	27	28	29

FEBRUARY

s	m	t	w	t	f	s
		1	2	3	4	5
6	7	8	9	10	11	12
13	14	15	16	17	18	19
20	21	22	23	24	25	26
27	28					

MARCH

s	m	t	w	t	f	s
		1	2	3	4	5
6	7	8	9	10	11	12
13	14	15	16	17	18	19
20	21	22	23	24	25	26
27	28	29	30	31		

APRIL

s	m	t	w	t	f	s
					1	2
3	4	5	6	7	8	9
10	11	12	13	14	15	16
17	18	19	20	21	22	23
24	25	26	27	28	29	30

MAY

s	m	t	w	t	f	s
1	2	3	4	5	6	7
8	9	10	11	12	13	14
15	16	17	18	19	20	21
22	23	24	25	26	27	28
29	30	31				

JUNE

s	m	t	w	t	f	s
			1	2	3	4
5	6	7	8	9	10	11
12	13	14	15	16	17	18
19	20	21	22	23	24	25
26	27	28	29	30		

JULY

s	m	t	w	t	f	s
					1	2
3	4	5	6	7	8	9
10	11	12	13	14	15	16
17	18	19	20	21	22	23
24/31	25	26	27	28	29	30

AUGUST

s	m	t	w	t	f	s
	1	2	3	4	5	6
7	8	9	10	11	12	13
14	15	16	17	18	19	20
21	22	23	24	25	26	27
28	29	30	31			

SEPTEMBER

s	m	t	w	t	f	s
				1	2	3
4	5	6	7	8	9	10
11	12	13	14	15	16	17
18	19	20	21	22	23	24
25	26	27	28	29	30	

OCTOBER

s	m	t	w	t	f	s
						1
2	3	4	5	6	7	8
9	10	11	12	13	14	15
16	17	18	19	20	21	22
23/30	24/31	25	26	27	28	29

NOVEMBER

s	m	t	w	t	f	s
		1	2	3	4	5
6	7	8	9	10	11	12
13	14	15	16	17	18	19
20	21	22	23	24	25	26
27	28	29	30			

DECEMBER

s	m	t	w	t	f	s
				1	2	3
4	5	6	7	8	9	10
11	12	13	14	15	16	17
18	19	20	21	22	23	24
25	26	27	28	29	30	31

January

SUNDAY	MONDAY	TUESDAY	WEDNESDAY	THURSDAY	FRIDAY	SATURDAY
						1
2	3 ☾	4	5	6	7	8
9	10 ●	11	12	13	14	15
16	17 ☽	18	19	20	21	22
23	24	25 ○	26	27	28	29
30	31					

JAN 1	NEW YEAR'S DAY	JAN 15	MARTIN LUTHER KING JR.'S BIRTHDAY
JAN 3	BANK HOLIDAY (U.K.)		
JAN 4	BANK HOLIDAY (SCOTLAND)	JAN 17	MARTIN LUTHER KING JR. DAY

February

SUNDAY	MONDAY	TUESDAY	WEDNESDAY	THURSDAY	FRIDAY	SATURDAY
		1	2 ☾	3	4	5
6	7	8 ●	9	10	11	12
13	14	15	16 ☽	17	18	19
20	21	22	23	24 ○	25	26
27	28					

FEB 9   ASH WEDNESDAY   FEB 21   PRESIDENTS' DAY

FEB 12   LINCOLN'S BIRTHDAY   FEB 22   WASHINGTON'S BIRTHDAY

FEB 14   VALENTINE'S DAY

March

SUNDAY	MONDAY	TUESDAY	WEDNESDAY	THURSDAY	FRIDAY	SATURDAY
		1	2	3 ☾	4	5
6	7	8	9	10 ●	11	12
13	14	15	16	17 ☽	18	19
20	21	22	23	24	25 ○	26
27	28	29	30	31		

MAR 6   MOTHERING SUNDAY (U.K.)
MAR 8   INTERNATIONAL WOMEN'S DAY
MAR 17 ST. PATRICK'S DAY
MAR 20 PALM SUNDAY
        VERNAL EQUINOX 12:33 P.M. (GMT)
MAR 24 PURIM (BEGINS AT SUNSET)
MAR 25 GOOD FRIDAY
MAR 27 EASTER SUNDAY
        SUMMER TIME BEGINS (U.K.)
MAR 28 EASTER MONDAY (CANADA, U.K.)

April

SUNDAY	MONDAY	TUESDAY	WEDNESDAY	THURSDAY	FRIDAY	SATURDAY
					1	2 ☾
3	4	5	6	7	8 ●	9
10	11	12	13	14	15	16 ☽
17	18	19	20	21	22	23
24 ○	25	26	27	28	29	30

APR 3   DAYLIGHT SAVING TIME BEGINS

APR 22 EARTH DAY

APR 23 PASSOVER (BEGINS AT SUNSET)

May

SUNDAY	MONDAY	TUESDAY	WEDNESDAY	THURSDAY	FRIDAY	SATURDAY
1 ☽	2	3	4	5	6	7
8 ●	9	10	11	12	13	14
15	16 ☽	17	18	19	20	21
22	23 ○	24	25	26	27	28
29	30 ☽	31				

MAY 2	BANK HOLIDAY (U.K.)		MAY 23	VICTORIA DAY (CANADA)
MAY 5	CINCO DE MAYO		MAY 30	MEMORIAL DAY
MAY 8	MOTHER'S DAY			BANK HOLIDAY (U.K.)
MAY 21	ARMED FORCES DAY			

June

SUNDAY	MONDAY	TUESDAY	WEDNESDAY	THURSDAY	FRIDAY	SATURDAY
			1	2	3	4
5	6 ●	7	8	9	10	11
12	13	14	15 ☽	16	17	18
19	20	21	22 ○	23	24	25
26	27	28 ☾	29	30		

JUN 14   FLAG DAY

JUN 19   FATHER'S DAY

JUN 21   SUMMER SOLSTICE 6:46 A.M. (GMT)

July

SUNDAY	MONDAY	TUESDAY	WEDNESDAY	THURSDAY	FRIDAY	SATURDAY
					1	2
3	4	5	6 ●	7	8	9
10	11	12	13	14 ☽	15	16
17	18	19	20	21 ○	22	23
24	25	26	27	28 ☾	29	30
31						

JUL 1   CANADA DAY (CANADA)
JUL 4   INDEPENDENCE DAY
JUL 12   BANK HOLIDAY (N. IRELAND)

August

SUNDAY	MONDAY	TUESDAY	WEDNESDAY	THURSDAY	FRIDAY	SATURDAY
	1	2	3	4	5 ●	6
7	8	9	10	11	12	13 ☽
14	15	16	17	18	19 ○	20
21	22	23	24	25	26 ☾	27
28	29	30	31			

AUG 1   CIVIC HOLIDAY (CANADA, MOST PROVINCES)
         BANK HOLIDAY (SCOTLAND)
AUG 29   BANK HOLIDAY (U.K. EXCEPT SCOTLAND)

September

SUNDAY	MONDAY	TUESDAY	WEDNESDAY	THURSDAY	FRIDAY	SATURDAY
				1	2	3 ●
4	5	6	7	8	9	10
11 ☽	12	13	14	15	16	17
18 ○	19	20	21	22	23	24
25 ☾	26	27	28	29	30	

SEP 5   LABOR DAY (U.S., CANADA)
SEP 22 AUTUMNAL EQUINOX 10:23 P.M. (GMT)

October

SUNDAY	MONDAY	TUESDAY	WEDNESDAY	THURSDAY	FRIDAY	SATURDAY
						1
2	3 ●	4	5	6	7	8
9	10 ☽	11	12	13	14	15
16	17 ○	18	19	20	21	22
23	24	25 ☾	26	27	28	29
30	31					

OCT 3   ROSH HASHANAH (BEGINS AT SUNSET)
OCT 10 COLUMBUS DAY OBSERVED
        THANKSGIVING DAY (CANADA)
OCT 12 COLUMBUS DAY
        YOM KIPPUR (BEGINS AT SUNSET)

OCT 24 UNITED NATIONS DAY
OCT 30 DAYLIGHT SAVING TIME ENDS
        SUMMER TIME ENDS (U.K.)
OCT 31 HALLOWEEN

November

SUNDAY	MONDAY	TUESDAY	WEDNESDAY	THURSDAY	FRIDAY	SATURDAY
		1	2 ●	3	4	5
6	7	8	9 ☽	10	11	12
13	14	15	16 ○	17	18	19
20	21	22	23 ☾	24	25	26
27	28	29	30			

NOV 11   VETERANS DAY
         REMEMBRANCE DAY (CANADA)
NOV 24   THANKSGIVING DAY

December

SUNDAY	MONDAY	TUESDAY	WEDNESDAY	THURSDAY	FRIDAY	SATURDAY
				1 ●	2	3
4	5	6	7	8 ☽	9	10
11	12	13	14	15 ○	16	17
18	19	20	21	22	23 ☾	24
25	26	27	28	29	30	31 ●

DEC 21   WINTER SOLSTICE 6:35 P.M. (GMT)   DEC 26   KWANZAA BEGINS
DEC 25   CHRISTMAS DAY   BOXING DAY (CANADA, U.K.)
         HANUKKAH (BEGINS AT SUNSET)   DEC 27   BANK HOLIDAY (U.K.)

White Flower, 1929

Oil on canvas, 76.2 x 91.5 cm (30 x 36 in.)
Cleveland Museum of Art
Hinman B. Hurlbut Collection, 2162.1930

BANK HOLIDAY (U.K.)

monday

27 362

BANK HOLIDAY (U.K.)

tuesday

28 363

wednesday

29 364

thursday

30 365

friday

31 366

NEW YEAR'S DAY

saturday

1 1

s	m	t	w	t	f	s
						1
2	3	4	5	6	7	8
9	10	11	12	13	14	15
16	17	18	19	20	21	22
23	24	25	26	27	28	29
30	31					

January

sunday

2 2

Morning Glory with Black, 1926

Oil on canvas, 91 x 75.5 cm (35$^{13}/_{16}$ x 29$^{3}/_{4}$ in.)
Cleveland Museum of Art
Bequest of Leonard C. Hanna, Jr. 1958.42

January

BANK HOLIDAY (U.K.)

monday

☽ **3** 3

BANK HOLIDAY (SCOTLAND)

tuesday

4 4

wednesday

5 5

thursday

6 6

friday

7 7

saturday

8 8

s	m	t	w	t	f	s
						1
2	3	4	5	6	7	8
9	10	11	12	13	14	15
16	17	18	19	20	21	22
23	24	25	26	27	28	29
30	31					

January

sunday

9 9

January

monday

10 **10** ●

tuesday

11 **11**

wednesday

12 **12**

thursday

13 **13**

friday

14 **14**

saturday

15 **15**

sunday

16 **16**

MARTIN LUTHER KING JR. DAY

monday
☽ **17** 17

tuesday
18 18

wednesday
19 19

thursday
20 20

friday
21 21

saturday
22 22

s	m	t	w	t	f	s
						1
2	3	4	5	6	7	8
9	10	11	12	13	14	15
16	17	18	19	20	21	22
23	24	25	26	27	28	29
30	31					

January

sunday
23 23

Sunflower, New Mexico, I, 1935

Oil on canvas, 50.8 x 40.6 cm (20 x 16 in.)
Cleveland Museum of Art
Bequest of Georgia O'Keeffe, 1987.140

January

tuesday

○**25** 25

wednesday

26 26

thursday

27 27

friday

28 28

saturday

29 29

s	m	t	w	t	f	s
						1
2	3	4	5	6	7	8
9	10	11	12	13	14	15
16	17	18	19	20	21	22
23	24	25	26	27	28	29
30	31					

January

sunday

30 30

January ~ February

31 **31**

32 **1**

33 **2** ☾

34 **3**

35 **4**

36 **5**

37 **6**

February

monday

7 38

tuesday

● **8** 39

ASH WEDNESDAY

wednesday

9 40

thursday

10 41

friday

11 42

LINCOLN'S BIRTHDAY

saturday

12 43

s	m	t	w	t	f	s
		1	2	3	4	5
6	7	8	9	10	11	12
13	14	15	16	17	18	19
20	21	22	23	24	25	26
27	28					

sunday

13 44

***Jimson Weed,* 1936–1937**

Oil on canvas, 177.8 x 212.1 cm (70 x 83½ in.)
Indianapolis Museum of Art
Gift of Eli Lilly and Company, IMA1997.131

February

VALENTINE'S DAY

monday

14 45

tuesday

15 46

wednesday

☽ **16** 47

thursday

17 48

friday

18 49

saturday

19 50

s	m	t	w	t	f	s
		1	2	3	4	5
6	7	8	9	10	11	12
13	14	15	16	17	18	19
20	21	22	23	24	25	26
27	28					

sunday

20 51

February

—————————————————————— PRESIDENTS' DAY

52 **21**

tuesday ————————————————————————— WASHINGTON'S BIRTHDAY

53 **22**

wednesday ———————————————————————————————————

54 **23**

thursday ————————————————————————————————————

55 **24** ○

friday ——————————————————————————————————————

56 **25**

saturday ——————————————————————————————————————

57 **26**

sunday ———————————————————————————————————————

58 **27**

monday

28 59

tuesday

1 60

wednesday

2 61

thursday

☾ **3** 62

friday

4 63

saturday

5 64

s	m	t	w	t	f	s
		1	2	3	4	5
6	7	8	9	10	11	12
13	14	15	16	17	18	19
20	21	22	23	24	25	26
27	28	29	30	31		

March

MOTHERING SUNDAY (U.K.)

sunday

6 65

***Purple Leaves,* 1922**

Oil on canvas on board, 22.9 x 30.5 cm (9 x 12 in.)
The Dayton Art Institute
Bequest of Virginia Rike Haswell, 1977.60

monday

7 66

tuesday

INTERNATIONAL WOMEN'S DAY

8 67

wednesday

9 68

thursday

●**10** 69

friday

11 70

saturday

12 71

s	m	t	w	t	f	s
		1	2	3	4	5
6	7	8	9	10	11	12
13	14	15	16	17	18	19
20	21	22	23	24	25	26
27	28	29	30	31		

sunday

13 72

March

Autumn Leaves—Lake George, N.Y., 1924

Oil on canvas, 51.4 x 41.3 cm (20¼ x 16¼ in.)
Columbus Museum of Art, Ohio
Museum Purchase, Howald Fund II, 1981.006

monday

14 ₇₃

tuesday

15 ₇₄

wednesday

16 ₇₅

ST. PATRICK'S DAY

thursday

☽ **17** ₇₆

friday

18 ₇₇

saturday

19 ₇₈

s	m	t	w	t	f	s
		1	2	3	4	5
6	7	8	9	10	11	12
13	14	15	16	17	18	19
20	21	22	23	24	25	26
27	28	29	30	31		

PALM SUNDAY

VERNAL EQUINOX 12:33 P.M. (GMT)

sunday

20 ₇₉

March

monday

₈₀ 21

tuesday

₈₁ 22

wednesday

₈₂ 23

thursday ———————————————————————— PURIM (BEGINS AT SUNSET)

₈₃ 24

friday ———————————————————————————————— GOOD FRIDAY

₈₄ 25 ○

saturday

₈₅ 26

sunday ———————————————————————————— EASTER SUNDAY

SUMMER TIME BEGINS (U.K.)

₈₆ 27

EASTER MONDAY (CANADA, U.K.)

monday
28 87

tuesday
29 88

wednesday
30 89

thursday
31 90

friday
1 91

saturday
☽ **2** 92

s	m	t	w	t	f	s
					1	2
3	4	5	6	7	8	9
10	11	12	13	14	15	16
17	18	19	20	21	22	23
24	25	26	27	28	29	30

April

DAYLIGHT SAVING TIME BEGINS

sunday
3 93

Coxcomb, **1931**

Oil on canvas, 50.8 x 43.2 cm (20 x 17 in.)
Pennsylvania Academy of the Fine Arts, Philadelphia
Partial gift and bequest of Mrs. Bernice McIlhenny Wintersteen, 1977.24.2

April

monday

4 94

tuesday

5 95

wednesday

6 96

thursday

7 97

friday

● **8** 98

saturday

9 99

s	m	t	w	t	f	s
					1	2
3	4	5	6	7	8	9
10	11	12	13	14	15	16
17	18	19	20	21	22	23
24	25	26	27	28	29	30

sunday

10 100

April

April

monday

101 **11**

tuesday

102 **12**

wednesday

103 **13**

thursday

104 **14**

friday

105 **15**

saturday

106 **16** ☽

sunday

107 **17**

April

tuesday

19 109

wednesday

20 110

thursday

21 111

EARTH DAY

friday

22 112

PASSOVER (BEGINS AT SUNSET)

saturday

23 113

s	m	t	w	t	f	s
					1	2
3	4	5	6	7	8	9
10	11	12	13	14	15	16
17	18	19	20	21	22	23
24	25	26	27	28	29	30

April

sunday

○ **24** 114

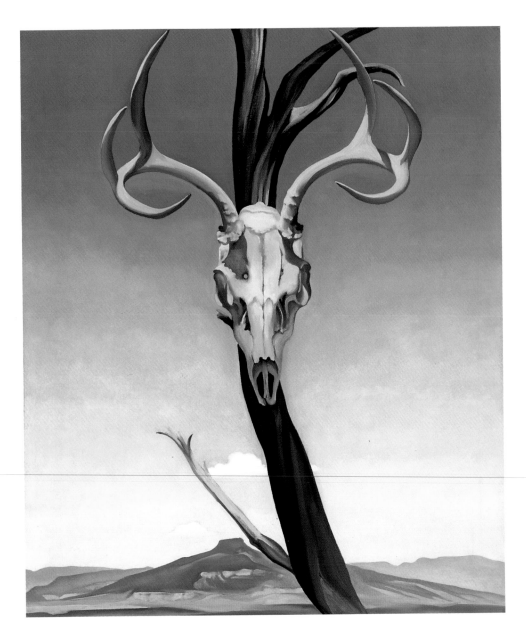

Deer's Skull with Pedernal, 1936

Oil on canvas, 91.4 x 76.5 cm (36 x 30⅛ in.)
Museum of Fine Arts, Boston
Gift of the William H. Lane Foundation, 1990.432

monday

25 115

tuesday

26 116

wednesday

27 117

thursday

28 118

friday

29 119

saturday

30 120

s	m	t	w	t	f	s
1	2	3	4	5	6	7
8	9	10	11	12	13	14
15	16	17	18	19	20	21
22	23	24	25	26	27	28
29	30	31				

May

sunday

☽ **1** 121

May

monday
2

BANK HOLIDAY (U.K.)

tuesday
123 **3**

wednesday
124 **4**

thursday
125 **5**

CINCO DE MAYO

friday
126 **6**

saturday
127 **7**

sunday
128 **8** ●

MOTHER'S DAY

May

monday

9 129

tuesday

10 130

wednesday

11 131

thursday

12 132

friday

13 133

saturday

14 134

s	m	t	w	t	f	s
1	2	3	4	5	6	7
8	9	10	11	12	13	14
15	16	17	18	19	20	21
22	23	24	25	26	27	28
29	30	31				

May

sunday

15 135

Series I, No. 3, **1918**

Oil on board, 50.8 x 40.6 cm (20 x 16 in.)
Milwaukee Art Museum
Gift of Jane Bradley Pettit Foundation and
The Georgia O'Keeffe Foundation, M1997.192
Photograph by Larry Sanders

May

monday
☽ **16** 136

tuesday
17 137

wednesday
18 138

thursday
19 139

friday
20 140

ARMED FORCES DAY

saturday
21 141

s	m	t	w	t	f	s
1	2	3	4	5	6	7
8	9	10	11	12	13	14
15	16	17	18	19	20	21
22	23	24	25	26	27	28
29	30	31				

sunday
22 142

May

May

monday
143 **23** ○

tuesday
144 **24**

wednesday
145 **25**

thursday
146 **26**

friday
147 **27**

saturday
148 **28**

sunday
149 **29**

May ~ June

MEMORIAL DAY

BANK HOLIDAY (U.K.)

monday

☽ **30** 150

tuesday

31 151

wednesday

1 152

thursday

2 153

friday

3 154

saturday

4 155

sunday

5 156

s	m	t	w	t	f	s
			1	2	3	4
5	6	7	8	9	10	11
12	13	14	15	16	17	18
19	20	21	22	23	24	25
26	27	28	29	30		

June

Lake George Barns, 1926

Oil on canvas, 53.8 x 81.4 cm (21³/₁₆ x 32¹/₁₆ in).
Walker Art Center, Minneapolis
Gift of the T. B. Walker Foundation, 1954

June

tuesday

7 ₁₅₈

wednesday

8 ₁₅₉

thursday

9 ₁₆₀

friday

10 ₁₆₁

saturday

11 ₁₆₂

sunday

12 ₁₆₃

s	m	t	w	t	f	s
			1	2	3	4
5	6	7	8	9	10	11
12	13	14	15	16	17	18
19	20	21	22	23	24	25
26	27	28	29	30		

Red Canna, **1925/1928**

Oil on canvas mounted on Masonite, 91.4 x 76 cm (36 x 29⁷/₈ in.)
The University of Arizona Museum of Art, Tucson
Gift of Oliver James, 50.1.4

June

monday

13 <small>164</small>

FLAG DAY

tuesday

14 <small>165</small>

wednesday

☽ ## 15 <small>166</small>

thursday

16 <small>167</small>

friday

17 <small>168</small>

saturday

18 <small>169</small>

s	m	t	w	t	f	s
			1	2	3	4
5	6	7	8	9	10	11
12	13	14	15	16	17	18
19	20	21	22	23	24	25
26	27	28	29	30		

June

FATHER'S DAY

sunday

19 <small>170</small>

June

monday

171 **20**

tuesday

SUMMER SOLSTICE 6:46 A.M. (GMT)

172 **21**

wednesday

173 **22** ○

thursday

174 **23**

friday

175 **24**

saturday

176 **25**

sunday

177 **26**

monday

27 178

tuesday

☾**28** 179

wednesday

29 180

thursday

30 181

CANADA DAY (CANADA)

friday

1 182

saturday

2 183

sunday

3 184

s	m	t	w	t	f	s
					1	2
3	4	5	6	7	8	9
10	11	12	13	14	15	16
17	18	19	20	21	22	23
24	25	26	27	28	29	30
31						

July

Gerald's Tree II, 1937

Oil on canvas, 101.6 x 76.2 cm (40 x 30 in.)
Stark Museum of Art, Orange, Texas
31.222/1

July

monday

4 185

tuesday

5 186

wednesday

● 6 187

thursday

7 188

friday

8 189

saturday

9 190

s	m	t	w	t	f	s
					1	2
3	4	5	6	7	8	9
10	11	12	13	14	15	16
17	18	19	20	21	22	23
24	25	26	27	28	29	30
31						

July

sunday

10 191

July

monday

₁₉₂ **11**

tuesday

BANK HOLIDAY (N. IRELAND)

₁₉₃ **12**

wednesday

₁₉₄ **13**

thursday

₁₉₅ **14** ☽

friday

₁₉₆ **15**

saturday

₁₉₇ **16**

sunday

₁₉₈ **17**

July

monday
18 199

tuesday
19 200

wednesday
20 201

thursday
○ **21** 202

friday
22 203

saturday
23 204

s	m	t	w	t	f	s
					1	2
3	4	5	6	7	8	9
10	11	12	13	14	15	16
17	18	19	20	21	22	23
24	25	26	27	28	29	30
31						

July

sunday
24 205

Poppy, 1927

Oil on canvas, 76.2 x 91.4 cm (30 x 36 in.)
Museum of Fine Arts, St. Petersburg, Florida
Gift of Charles C. and Margaret Stevenson Henderson
in memory of Jeanne Crawford Henderson, 71.32

monday

25 206

tuesday

26 207

wednesday

27 208

thursday

☽ **28** 209

friday

29 210

saturday

30 211

s	m	t	w	t	f	s
					1	2
3	4	5	6	7	8	9
10	11	12	13	14	15	16
17	18	19	20	21	22	23
24	25	26	27	28	29	30
31						

July

sunday

31 212

August

monday

213 1

CIVIC HOLIDAY (CANADA, MOST PROVINCES)

BANK HOLIDAY (SCOTLAND)

tuesday

214 2

wednesday

215 3

thursday

216 4

friday

217 5 ●

saturday

218 6

sunday

219 7

August

monday

8 220

tuesday

9 221

wednesday

10 222

thursday

11 223

friday

12 224

saturday

☽**13** 225

s	m	t	w	t	f	s
	1	2	3	4	5	6
7	8	9	10	11	12	13
14	15	16	17	18	19	20
21	22	23	24	25	26	27
28	29	30	31			

August

sunday

14 226

Red Hills, Lake George, 1927

Oil on canvas, 68.6 x 81.3 cm (27 x 32 in.)
Acquired 1945
The Phillips Collection, Washington, D.C.

monday

15 ₂₂₇

tuesday

16 ₂₂₈

wednesday

17 ₂₂₉

thursday

18 ₂₃₀

friday

○**19** ₂₃₁

saturday

20 ₂₃₂

s	m	t	w	t	f	s
	1	2	3	4	5	6
7	8	9	10	11	12	13
14	15	16	17	18	19	20
21	22	23	24	25	26	27
28	29	30	31			

sunday

21 ₂₃₃

August

monday

234   **22**

tuesday

235   **23**

wednesday

236   **24**

thursday

237   **25**

friday

238   **26** ☾

saturday

239   **27**

sunday

240   **28**

BANK HOLIDAY (U.K. EXCEPT SCOTLAND)

monday
29 241

tuesday
30 242

wednesday
31 243

thursday
1 244

friday
2 245

saturday
●**3** 246

sunday
4 247

s	m	t	w	t	f	s
				1	2	3
4	5	6	7	8	9	10
11	12	13	14	15	16	17
18	19	20	21	22	23	24
25	26	27	28	29	30	

September

***My Shanty, Lake George,* 1922**

Oil on canvas, 50.8 x 68.9 cm (20 x 27⅛ in.)
Acquired 1926
The Phillips Collection, Washington, D.C.

September

LABOR DAY (U.S., CANADA)

monday

5 ₂₄₈

tuesday

6 ₂₄₉

wednesday

7 ₂₅₀

thursday

8 ₂₅₁

friday

9 ₂₅₂

saturday

10 ₂₅₃

s	m	t	w	t	f	s
				1	2	3
4	5	6	7	8	9	10
11	12	13	14	15	16	17
18	19	20	21	22	23	24
25	26	27	28	29	30	

September

sunday

☽ 11 ₂₅₄

Red Canna, 1923

Oil on canvas, 30.5 x 25.1 cm (12 x 9⅞ in.)
Pennsylvania Academy of the Fine Arts, Philadelphia
The Vivian O. and Meyer P. Potamkin Collection
Estate of Vivian O. Potamkin, 2003.1.8

September

s	m	t	w	t	f	s
				1	2	3
4	5	6	7	8	9	10
11	12	13	14	15	16	17
18	19	20	21	22	23	24
25	26	27	28	29	30	

September

September

monday
₂₆₂ **19**

tuesday
₂₆₃ **20**

wednesday
₂₆₄ **21**

thursday
AUTUMNAL EQUINOX 10:23 P.M. (GMT)
₂₆₅ **22**

friday
₂₆₆ **23**

saturday
₂₆₇ **24**

sunday
₂₆₈ **25** ☾

monday

26 269

tuesday

27 270

wednesday

28 271

thursday

29 272

friday

30 273

saturday

1 274

sunday

2 275

s	m	t	w	t	f	s
						1
2	3	4	5	6	7	8
9	10	11	12	13	14	15
16	17	18	19	20	21	22
23	24	25	26	27	28	29
30	31					

October

White Iris, 1930
Oil on canvas, 101.6 x 76.2 cm (40 x 30 in.)
Virginia Museum of Fine Arts, Richmond
Gift of Mr. and Mrs. Bruce C. Gottwald
Photograph by Katherine Wetzel
© Virginia Museum of Fine Arts

ROSH HASHANAH (BEGINS AT SUNSET)

monday
● **3** 276

tuesday
4 277

wednesday
5 278

thursday
6 279

friday
7 280

saturday
8 281

sunday
9 282

s	m	t	w	t	f	s
						1
2	3	4	5	6	7	8
9	10	11	12	13	14	15
16	17	18	19	20	21	22
23	24	25	26	27	28	29
30	31					

October

October

monday

283   10 ☽

tuesday

284   11

wednesday

285   12

thursday

286   13

friday

287   14

saturday

288   15

sunday

289   16

October

monday
○ **17** 290

tuesday
18 291

wednesday
19 292

thursday
20 293

friday
21 294

saturday
22 295

s	m	t	w	t	f	s
						1
2	3	4	5	6	7	8
9	10	11	12	13	14	15
16	17	18	19	20	21	22
23	24	25	26	27	28	29
30	31					

October

sunday
23 296

***Squash Flowers No. 1*, 1925**

Oil on cardboard, 45.9 x 35 cm (18$^{1}/_{16}$ x 13$^{3}/_{4}$ in.)
Smith College Museum of Art, Northampton, Massachusetts
Gift of Mr. and Mrs. Allan D. Emil, 1955

UNITED NATIONS DAY

monday
24 297

tuesday
☾ 25 298

wednesday
26 299

thursday
27 300

friday
28 301

saturday
29 302

s	m	t	w	t	f	s
						1
2	3	4	5	6	7	8
9	10	11	12	13	14	15
16	17	18	19	20	21	22
23	24	25	26	27	28	29
30	31					

October

DAYLIGHT SAVING TIME ENDS

SUMMER TIME ENDS (U.K.)

sunday
30 303

October ~ November

monday ——————————————————————————— HALLOWEEN
31

tuesday ———————————————————————————
1

wednesday ———————————————————————————
2 ●

thursday ———————————————————————————
3

friday ———————————————————————————
4

saturday ———————————————————————————
5

sunday ———————————————————————————
6

monday

7 311

tuesday

8 312

wednesday

☽ **9** 313

thursday

10 314

VETERANS DAY

REMEMBRANCE DAY (CANADA)

friday

11 315

saturday

12 316

s	m	t	w	t	f	s
		1	2	3	4	5
6	7	8	9	10	11	12
13	14	15	16	17	18	19
20	21	22	23	24	25	26
27	28	29	30			

sunday

13 317

November

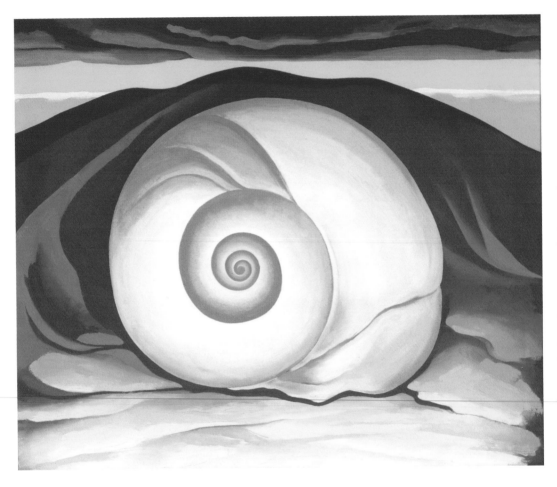

Red Hills with White Shell, 1938

Oil on canvas, 76.2 x 92.7 cm (30 x 36½ in.)
The Museum of Fine Arts, Houston
Gift of Isabel B. Wilson in memory of her mother, Alice Pratt Brown
91.2027

November

tuesday

15 319

wednesday

○ **16** 320

thursday

17 321

friday

18 322

saturday

19 323

s	m	t	w	t	f	s
		1	2	3	4	5
6	7	8	9	10	11	12
13	14	15	16	17	18	19
20	21	22	23	24	25	26
27	28	29	30			

sunday

20 324

November

November

monday

325 **21**

tuesday

326 **22**

wednesday

327 **23** ☽

thursday   THANKSGIVING DAY

328 **24**

friday

329 **25**

saturday

330 **26**

sunday

331 **27**

November ~ December

monday

28 <small>332</small>

tuesday

29 <small>333</small>

wednesday

30 <small>334</small>

thursday

● **1** <small>335</small>

friday

2 <small>336</small>

saturday

3 <small>337</small>

sunday

4 <small>338</small>

s	m	t	w	t	f	s
				1	2	3
4	5	6	7	8	9	10
11	12	13	14	15	16	17
18	19	20	21	22	23	24
25	26	27	28	29	30	31

December

Lake George with Crows, 1921

Oil on canvas, 72 x 63.2 cm (28⅜ x 24⅞ in.)

National Gallery of Canada, Ottawa

Gift of the Georgia O'Keeffe Foundation, Abiquiu, New Mexico, 1995

37690

December

monday

5 339

tuesday

6 340

wednesday

7 341

thursday

☾ **8** 342

friday

9 343

saturday

10 344

sunday

11 345

s	m	t	w	t	f	s
				1	2	3
4	5	6	7	8	9	10
11	12	13	14	15	16	17
18	19	20	21	22	23	24
25	26	27	28	29	30	31

December

December

monday

346 **12**

tuesday

347 **13**

wednesday

348 **14**

thursday

349 **15** ○

friday

350 **16**

saturday

351 **17**

sunday

352 **18**

December

monday
19 353

tuesday
20 354

WINTER SOLSTICE 6:35 P.M. (GMT)

wednesday
21 355

thursday
22 356

friday
☾ 23 357

saturday
24 358

s	m	t	w	t	f	s
				1	2	3
4	5	6	7	8	9	10
11	12	13	14	15	16	17
18	19	20	21	22	23	24
25	26	27	28	29	30	31

December

CHRISTMAS DAY

HANUKKAH (BEGINS AT SUNSET)

sunday
25 359

December ~ January

tuesday

361 27

BANK HOLIDAY (U.K.)

wednesday

362 28

thursday

363 29

friday

364 30

saturday

365 31 ●

sunday

1 1

NEW YEAR'S DAY

January

BANK HOLIDAY (U.K.)

monday

2 _2_

BANK HOLIDAY (SCOTLAND)

tuesday

3 _3_

wednesday

4 _4_

thursday

5 _5_

friday

☽ 6 _6_

saturday

7 _7_

s	m	t	w	t	f	s
1	2	3	4	5	6	7
8	9	10	11	12	13	14
15	16	17	18	19	20	21
22	23	24	25	26	27	28
29	30	31				

sunday

8 _8_

January

2006

JANUARY

s	m	t	w	t	f	s
1	2	3	4	5	6	7
8	9	10	11	12	13	14
15	16	17	18	19	20	21
22	23	24	25	26	27	28
29	30	31				

FEBRUARY

s	m	t	w	t	f	s
			1	2	3	4
5	6	7	8	9	10	11
12	13	14	15	16	17	18
19	20	21	22	23	24	25
26	27	28				

MARCH

s	m	t	w	t	f	s
			1	2	3	4
5	6	7	8	9	10	11
12	13	14	15	16	17	18
19	20	21	22	23	24	25
26	27	28	29	30	31	

APRIL

s	m	t	w	t	f	s
						1
2	3	4	5	6	7	8
9	10	11	12	13	14	15
16	17	18	19	20	21	22
23/30	24	25	26	27	28	29

MAY

s	m	t	w	t	f	s
	1	2	3	4	5	6
7	8	9	10	11	12	13
14	15	16	17	18	19	20
21	22	23	24	25	26	27
28	29	30	31			

JUNE

s	m	t	w	t	f	s
				1	2	3
4	5	6	7	8	9	10
11	12	13	14	15	16	17
18	19	20	21	22	23	24
25	26	27	28	29	30	

2006

JULY

s	m	t	w	t	f	s
						1
2	3	4	5	6	7	8
9	10	11	12	13	14	15
16	17	18	19	20	21	22
23/30	24/31	25	26	27	28	29

AUGUST

s	m	t	w	t	f	s
		1	2	3	4	5
6	7	8	9	10	11	12
13	14	15	16	17	18	19
20	21	22	23	24	25	26
27	28	29	30	31		

SEPTEMBER

s	m	t	w	t	f	s
					1	2
3	4	5	6	7	8	9
10	11	12	13	14	15	16
17	18	19	20	21	22	23
24	25	26	27	28	29	30

OCTOBER

s	m	t	w	t	f	s
1	2	3	4	5	6	7
8	9	10	11	12	13	14
15	16	17	18	19	20	21
22	23	24	25	26	27	28
29	30	31				

NOVEMBER

s	m	t	w	t	f	s
			1	2	3	4
5	6	7	8	9	10	11
12	13	14	15	16	17	18
19	20	21	22	23	24	25
26	27	28	29	30		

DECEMBER

s	m	t	w	t	f	s
					1	2
3	4	5	6	7	8	9
10	11	12	13	14	15	16
17	18	19	20	21	22	23
24/31	25	26	27	28	29	30

Following are major (bank-closing) holidays for selected countries in 2005. Islamic observances are subject to adjustment. Holidays for the U.S., U.K., and Canada and major Jewish holidays appear on this calendar's grid pages. Pomegranate is not responsible for errors or omissions in this list. Users of this information should confirm dates with local sources before making international travel or business plans.

ARGENTINA

1	Jan	New Year's Day
24	Mar	Holy Thursday
25	Mar	Good Friday
27	Mar	Easter
4	Apr	Malvinas Islands Memorial
1	May	Labor Day
25	May	National Holiday
20	Jun	Flag Day
9	Jul	Independence Day
15	Aug	Gen. San Martín Anniversary
10	Oct	Columbus Day
8	Dec	Immaculate Conception
25	Dec	Christmas

AUSTRALIA

1–3	Jan	New Year's Holiday
26	Jan	Australia Day
7	Mar	Labor Day (Western Australia)
14	Mar	Labor Day (Victoria)
25	Mar	Good Friday
26	Mar	Easter Saturday (New South Wales)
27–28	Mar	Easter Holiday
25	Apr	Anzac Day
2	May	Labor Day (Queensland)
13	Jun	Queen's Birthday
1	Aug	Bank Holiday (New South Wales, Northern Territory)
3	Oct	Labor Day (New South Wales, Australian Capital Territory, and South Australia)
1	Nov	Melbourne Cup Day (Victoria)
25–26	Dec	Christmas Holiday
27	Dec	Boxing Day

BRAZIL

1	Jan	New Year's Day
20	Jan	Foundation Day (Rio de Janeiro)
25	Jan	Foundation Day (São Paulo)
7–8	Feb	Carnival
25	Mar	Good Friday
27	Mar	Easter
21	Apr	Tiradentes Day
1	May	Labor Day
26	May	Corpus Christi
9	Jul	Civic Holiday (São Paulo)
7	Sep	Independence Day
12	Oct	Our Lady of Aparecida
2	Nov	All Souls' Day
15	Nov	Proclamation of the Republic
25	Dec	Christmas
31	Dec	New Year's Eve

CHINA (SEE ALSO HONG KONG)

1	Jan	New Year's Day
9–11	Feb	Lunar New Year
1–3	May	Labor Day Holiday
1–3	Oct	National Holiday

FRANCE

1	Jan	New Year's Day
25	Mar	Good Friday
27–28	Mar	Easter Holiday
1	May	Labor Day
8	May	Armistice Day (1)
5	May	Ascension Day
16	May	Whitmonday
14	Jul	Bastille Day
15	Aug	Assumption Day
1	Nov	All Saints' Day
11	Nov	Armistice Day (2)
25	Dec	Christmas

GERMANY

1	Jan	New Year's Day
6	Jan	Epiphany (Munich)
25	Mar	Good Friday
27–28	Mar	Easter Holiday
1	May	Labor Day
5	May	Ascension Day
16	May	Whitmonday
26	May	Corpus Christi
15	Aug	Assumption Day (Munich)
3	Oct	National Day
1	Nov	All Saints' Day (Munich)
24	Dec	Christmas Eve
25	Dec	Christmas
26	Dec	Boxing Day
31	Dec	New Year's Eve

HONG KONG

1	Jan	New Year's Day
9–11	Feb	Lunar New Year
25–28	Mar	Easter Holiday
5	Apr	Ching Ming Festival
1	May	Labor Day
15	May	Buddha's Birthday
11	Jun	Tuen Ng Day
1	Jul	SAR Establishment Day
19	Sep	Mid-Autumn Festival
1	Oct	Chinese National Holiday
11	Oct	Chung Yeung Day
25–27	Dec	Christmas Holiday

INDIA

21	Jan	Bakr-Id (Eid-al-Adha)
26	Jan	Republic Day
19	Feb	Muharram
25	Mar	Good Friday
27	Mar	Easter
1	Apr	Half-yearly bank closing
21	Apr	Prophet Muhammad's Birthday
1	May	Maharashtra Day (Mumbai)
15	Aug	Independence Day
30	Sep	Half-yearly bank closing
2	Oct	Mahatma Gandhi's Birthday
1	Nov	Diwali (Deepavali)
3	Nov	Ramzan Id (Eid-al-Fitr)
25	Dec	Christmas

(Additional holidays to be declared)

IRELAND

1	Jan	New Year's Day
17	Mar	St. Patrick's Day
25	Mar	Good Friday
27–28	Mar	Easter Holiday
2	May	May Day
6	Jun	Summer Holiday
1	Aug	Autumn Holiday
31	Oct	Halloween
25	Dec	Christmas
26	Dec	St. Stephen's Day

ISRAEL

25	Mar	Purim
24	Apr	First day of Pesach
30	Apr	Last day of Pesach
14	May	National Independence Day
13	Jun	Shavuot
14	Aug	Fast of Av
4–5	Oct	Rosh Hashanah
13	Oct	Yom Kippur
18	Oct	First day of Sukkot
25	Oct	Shemini Atzeret

ITALY

1	Jan	New Year's Day
6	Jan	Epiphany
27–28	Mar	Easter Holiday
25	Apr	Liberation Day
1	May	Labor Day
2	Jun	Republic Day
29	Jun	Sts. Peter and Paul (Rome)
15	Aug	Assumption Day
1	Nov	All Saints' Day
8	Dec	Immaculate Conception
25	Dec	Christmas
26	Dec	St. Stephen's Day

JAPAN

1 Jan	New Year's Day
10 Jan	Coming of Age Day
11 Feb	National Foundation Day
21 Mar	Vernal Equinox Holiday
29 Apr	Greenery Day
3 May	Constitution Day
4 May	National Holiday
5 May	Children's Day
20 Jul	Marine Day
19 Sep	Respect for the Aged Day
23 Sep	Autumnal Equinox Holiday
10 Oct	Health and Sports Day
3 Nov	Culture Day
23 Nov	Labor Thanksgiving Day
23 Dec	Emperor's Birthday
31 Dec	New Year's Eve

KENYA

1 Jan	New Year's Day
25 Mar	Good Friday
27–28 Mar	Easter Holiday
1 May	Labor Day
1 Jun	Madaraka Day
10 Oct	Moi Day
20 Oct	Kenyatta Day
4 Nov	Eid-al-Fitr
12 Dec	Jamhuri Day
25 Dec	Christmas
26 Dec	Boxing Day

MALAYSIA

1 Jan	New Year's Day
21 Jan	Hari Raya Haji (Eid-al-Adha)
1 Feb	Federal Territory Day
9–10 Feb	Lunar New Year
10 Feb	First day of Muharram
21 Apr	Prophet Muhammad's Birthday
1 May	Labor Day
23 May	Vesak Day (Buddha's Birthday)
4 Jun	Yang DiPertuan Agong's Birthday
31 Aug	National Day
1 Nov	Deepavali
3–4 Nov	Hari Raya Puasa (Eid-al-Fitr)
25 Dec	Christmas

MEXICO

1 Jan	New Year's Day
5 Feb	Constitution Day
21 Mar	Benito Juárez's Birthday
24 Mar	Holy Thursday
25 Mar	Good Friday
26 Mar	Holy Saturday
27 Mar	Easter
1 May	Labor Day
5 May	Battle of Puebla

1 Sep	Bank Holiday
16 Sep	Independence Day
20 Nov	Revolution Day
12 Dec	Our Lady of Guadalupe
25 Dec	Christmas

NETHERLANDS

1 Jan	New Year's Day
25 Mar	Good Friday
27–28 Mar	Easter Holiday
30 Apr	Queen's Birthday
5 May	Ascension Day/Liberation Day
16 May	Whitmonday
25 Dec	Christmas
26 Dec	Boxing Day

NEW ZEALAND

1–4 Jan	New Year's Holiday
24 Jan	Wellington Provincial Anniversary
31 Jan	Auckland Provincial Anniversary
6 Feb	Waitangi Day
25 Mar	Good Friday
27–28 Mar	Easter Holiday
25 Apr	Anzac Day
6 Jun	Queen's Birthday
24 Oct	Labor Day
25–26 Dec	Christmas Holiday
27 Dec	Boxing Day

PUERTO RICO

1 Jan	New Year's Day
6 Jan	Three Kings Day (Epiphany)
11 Jan	Eugenio María de Hostos's Birthday
17 Jan	Martin Luther King Jr. Day
21 Feb	Presidents' Day
22 Mar	Emancipation Day
25 Mar	Good Friday
27 Mar	Easter
16 Apr	José de Diego's Birthday
30 May	Memorial Day
24 Jun	St. John the Baptist
4 Jul	U.S. Independence Day
17 Jul	Luís Muñoz Rivera's Birthday
25 Jul	Constitution Day
27 Jul	José Celso Barbosa's Birthday
5 Sep	Labor Day
10 Oct	Columbus Day
11 Nov	Veterans Day
19 Nov	Discovery of Puerto Rico
24 Nov	Thanksgiving Day
25 Dec	Christmas

SAUDI ARABIA

16–24 Jan	Eid-al-Adha
29 Oct–8 Nov	Eid-al-Fitr

SINGAPORE

1 Jan	New Year's Day
21 Jan	Hari Raya Haji (Eid-al-Adha)
9–11 Feb	Lunar New Year
25 Mar	Good Friday
27 Mar	Easter
1 May	Labor Day
23 May	Vesak Day (Buddha's Birthday)
9 Aug	National Day
1 Nov	Deepavali
3 Nov	Hari Raya Puasa (Eid-al-Fitr)
25 Dec	Christmas

SOUTH AFRICA

1 Jan	New Year's Day
21 Mar	Human Rights Day
25 Mar	Good Friday
27 Mar	Easter
28 Mar	Family Day
27 Apr	Freedom Day
1 May	Labor Day
16 Jun	Youth Day
9 Aug	National Women's Day
24 Sep	Heritage Day
16 Dec	Day of Reconciliation
25 Dec	Christmas
26 Dec	Day of Goodwill

SPAIN

1 Jan	New Year's Day
6 Jan	Epiphany
24 Mar	Holy Thursday
25 Mar	Good Friday
27 Mar	Easter
1 May	Labor Day
2 May	Independence Day
15 May	San Isidro's Day
15 Aug	Assumption Day
12 Oct	Hispanity Day
1 Nov	All Saints' Day
9 Nov	Our Lady of Almudena
6 Dec	Constitution Day
8 Dec	Immaculate Conception
25 Dec	Christmas

SWITZERLAND

1 Jan	New Year's Day
2 Jan	Berchtoldstag
25 Mar	Good Friday
27–28 Mar	Easter Holiday
1 May	Labor Day
5 May	Ascension Day
16 May	Whitmonday
1 Aug	National Day
25 Dec	Christmas
26 Dec	St. Stephen's Day

- From the U.S., dial 011 (international access code), country code, city code, and local telephone number.
- Numbers listed alongside country names are country codes.
- Numbers listed alongside city names are city codes; an asterisk (*) means that no city code is needed.
- Numbers in parentheses indicate hourly differences from Pacific Standard Time. A range of numbers indicates a country with more than one time zone.

Albania 355	(+9)	
Tirana 42		
Algeria 213	(+9)	
Algiers 2		
Argentina 54	(+5)	
Buenos Aires 11		
Córdoba 351		
Santa Fé 342		
Armenia 374	(+12)	
Aparan 520		
Talin 490		
Aruba 297	(+4)	
All cities 8 + 5 digits		
Australia 61	(+16–18)	
Adelaide 8		
Brisbane 7		
Canberra 2		
Melbourne 3		
Perth 8		
Sydney 2		
Austria 43	(+9)	
Salzburg 662		
Vienna 1		
Bangladesh 880	(+14)	
Chittagong 31		
Dhaka 2		
Khulna 41		
Belgium 32	(+9)	
Antwerp 3		
Brussels 2		
Ghent 9		
Bolivia 591	(+4)	
La Paz 2		
Santa Cruz 3		
Bosnia-Herzegovina .. 387	(+9)	
Sarajevo 33		
Brazil 55	(+3–6)	
Brasília 61		
Porto Alegre 51		
Rio de Janeiro 21		
Salvador 71		
São Paulo 11		
Bulgaria 359	(+10)	
Sofia 2		
Cambodia 855	(+15)	
Phnom Penh 23 or 22		
Cameroon 237*	(+9)	
Central African Republic 236*	(+9)	
Chile 56	(+4)	
Concepción 41		
Santiago 2		
Valparaíso 32		

China 86	(+16)	
Beijing 10		
Canton (Guangzhou) 20		
Fuzhou 591		
Shanghai 21		
Colombia 57	(+3)	
Bogotá 1		
Cali 2		
Medellín 4		
Congo 242*	(+9)	
Congo, Democratic		
Republic of 243	(+9–10)	
Kinshasa 12		
Costa Rica 506*	(+2)	
Croatia 385	(+9)	
Dubrovnik 20		
Zagreb 1		
Cuba 53	(+3)	
Cyprus 357	(+10)	
Nicosia 22		
Czech Republic 420	(+9)	
Prague 2		
Denmark 45*	(+9)	
Ecuador 593	(+3)	
Guayaquil 4		
Quito 2		
Egypt 20	(+10)	
Alexandria 3		
Cairo 2		
El Salvador 503	(+2)	
Estonia 372	(+10)	
Tallinn 6		
Ethiopia 251	(+11)	
Addis Ababa 1		
Fiji 679*	(+20)	
Finland 358	(+10)	
Helsinki 9		
France 33	(+9)	
Bordeaux 556		
Cannes 493		
Grenoble 476		
Marseille 491		
Nice 493		
Paris 1		
Toulouse 561		
French Antilles 590*	(+4)	
French Polynesia ... 689*	(-1--2)	
(Moorea and Tahiti)		
Georgia 995	(+12)	
Tbilisi 32		
Germany 49	(+9)	
Berlin 30		
Frankfurt 69		
Hamburg 40		
Munich 89		
Gibraltar 350*	(+9)	
Greece 30	(+10)	
Athens 1		
Iráklion (Crete) 81		
Guam 671*	(+18)	
Guantánamo Bay 53	(+3)	
(U.S. Naval Base)		
All points 99		

Guatemala 502*	(+2)	
Haiti 509*	(+3)	
Honduras 504*	(+2)	
Hong Kong 852*	(+16)	
Hungary 36	(+9)	
Budapest 1		
Debrecen 52		
Iceland 354	(+8)	
Keflavík Naval Base 2		
Reykjavík 1		
India 91	(+13.5)	
Bombay 22		
Calcutta 33		
Madras 44		
New Delhi 11		
Indonesia 62	(+15–17)	
Jakarta 21		
Iran 98	(+11.5)	
Esfahan 311		
Shiraz 711		
Tehran 21		
Iraq 964	(+11)	
Arbil 66		
Baghdad 1		
Mousil 60		
Ireland 353	(+8)	
Cork 21		
Dublin 1		
Israel 972	(+10)	
Haifa 4		
Jerusalem 2		
Tel Aviv 3		
Italy 39	(+9)	
Florence 055		
Genoa 010		
Milan 02		
Naples 081		
Rome 06		
Venice 041		
Ivory Coast 225*	(+8)	
Japan 81	(+17)	
Kyoto 75		
Tokyo 3		
Yokohama 45		
Jordan 962	(+10)	
Amman 6		
Karak 3		
Kenya 254	(+11)	
Mombasa 11		
Nairobi 2		
N. Korea 850	(+17)	
S. Korea 82	(+17)	
Kwangju 62		
Pusan 51		
Seoul 2		
Taegu 53		
Kuwait 965*	(+11)	
Laos 856	(+15)	
Vientiane 21		
Latvia 371	(+10)	
Riga 2		
Lebanon 961	(+10)	
Beirut 1		

Liberia ....231* (+8)	Peru ....51 (+3)	Tainan 6
Libya ....218 (+10)	Arequipa 54	Taipei 2
Tripoli 21	Lima 1	Tanzania ....255 (+11)
Liechtenstein ....41 (+9)	Philippines ....63 (+16)	Dar es Salaam 22
Lithuania ....370 (+10)	Bacolod 34	Tanga 27
Kaunas 37	Cebu City 32	Thailand ....66 (+15)
Luxembourg ....352* (+9)	Davao 82	Bangkok 2
Macau ....853* (+16)	Iloilo City 33	Chanthaburi 39
Macedonia ....389 (+9)	Manila 2	Tunisia ....216 (+9)
Malaysia ....60 (+16)	Poland ....48 (+9)	Bizerte 2
Ipoh 5	Gdansk 58	Tunis 1
Kuala Lumpur 3	Krakow 12	Turkey ....90 (+10)
Mexico ....52 (+0-2)	Warsaw 22	Ankara 312
Acapulco 744	Portugal ....351 (+8)	Istanbul
Cabo San Lucas 624	Lisbon 21	Asian 216
Cancún 998	Romania ....40 (+10)	European 212
Ciudad Juárez 656	Bucharest 21	Uganda ....256 (+11)
Ensenada 646	Russia ....7 (+10-20)	Entebbe 42
Guadalajara 33	Moscow 095	Kampala 41
La Paz 612	St. Petersburg 812	Ukraine ....380 (+10)
Mazatlán 669	Saudi Arabia ....966 (+11)	Kiev 44
Mexicali 686	Jeddah 2	Lvov 322
Mexico City 55	Mecca (Makkah) 2	United Arab Emirates. .971 (+12)
Monterrey 81	Riyadh 1	Abu Dhabi 2
Tijuana 666	Senegal ....221 (+8)	Ajman 6
Veracruz 229	Dakar 8	Al Ain 3
Monaco ....377* (+9)	Singapore ....65 (+16)	Fujairah 70
Morocco ....212 (+8)	Slovakia ....421 (+9)	United Kingdom .....44 (+8)
Marrakech 44	Bratislava 2	Belfast 28
Rabat 37	Slovenia ....386 (+9)	Birmingham 121
Mozambique ....258 (+10)	Ljubljana 1	Cardiff 29
Maputo 1	Maribor 2	Edinburgh 131
Myanmar ....95 (+14.5)	South Africa ....27 (+10)	Glasgow 141
Rangoon (Yangon) 1	Bloemfontein 51	Liverpool 151
Namibia ....264 (+9)	Cape Town 21	London 20
Windhoek 61	Durban 31	Manchester 161
Nepal ....977 (+14)	Johannesburg 11	Southampton 23
Kathmandu 1	Pretoria 12	Uruguay ....598 (+5)
Netherlands ....31 (+9)	Spain ....34 (+9)	Canelones 332
Amsterdam 20	Barcelona 93	Mercedes 532
The Hague (Den Haag) 70	Granada 958	Montevideo 2
Rotterdam 10	Madrid 91	Vatican City ....39 (+9)
Netherlands Antilles. .599 (+4)	Palma de Mallorca 971	All points 6
St. Maarten 5	Pamplona 948	Venezuela ....58 (+4)
New Zealand ....64 (+20-21)	Seville 95	Caracas 212
Auckland 9	Valencia 96	Maracaibo 261
Christchurch 3	Sri Lanka ....94 (+14)	Maracay 243
Wellington 4	Columbo Central 1	Valencia 241
Nicaragua ....505 (+2)	Suriname ....597* (+5)	Vietnam ....84 (+15)
León 311	Sweden ....46 (+9)	Hanoi 4
Managua 2	Malmo 40	Ho Chi Minh City 8
Nigeria ....234 (+9)	Stockholm 8	Yemen ....967 (+11)
Lagos 1	Switzerland ....41 (+9)	Aden 2
Norway ....47* (+9)	Basel 61	Sana'a 1
Pakistan ....92 (+13)	Berne 31	Zabid 3
Islamabad 51	Geneva 22	Yugoslavia (Serbia and
Karachi 21	Lausanne 21	Montenegro) .....381 (+9)
Lahore 42	Lucerne 41	Belgrade 11
Panama ....507* (+3)	Zürich 1	Cetinje 86
Paraguay ....595 (+4)	Syria ....963 (+10)	Zambia ....260 (+10)
Asunción 21	Damascus 11	Lusaka 1
Concepción 31	Taiwan ....886 (+16)	Zimbabwe ....263 (+10)
	Kao-hsiung 7	Harare 4

Notes

Notes

January

February

March

May

June

July

NOTES/EXPENSES

August

September

October

November

December

PERSONAL INFORMATION

name _____

address _____

city _____ state _____ zip _____

phone _____

cell/pgr _____ fax _____

e-mail _____

in case of emergency, please notify:

name _____

address _____

city _____ state _____ zip _____

phone _____

physician's name _____

physician's phone _____

health insurance company _____

plan number _____

allergies _____

other _____

driver's license number _____

car insurance company _____

policy number _____